NIGEL HAD SPOTTED THE PRINTING
ERROR JUST A LITTLE TOO LATE...

TRUNDLING GRUNTS

GLEN BAXTER

BLOOMSBURY

THIS BOOK IS DEDICATED TO ALL THOSE
WHO HAVE FORSWORN SUEDE AND
ESCHEWED THE GOATEE IN ALL ITS FORMS

First published in Great Britain 2002

Copyright © 2002 by Glen Baxter

The moral right of the author has been asserted

Bloomsbury Publishing Plc, 38 Soho Square, London W1D 3HB

ISBN 0 7475 6057 9

10 9 8 7 6 5 4 3 2 1

Printed and bound in Italy by Artegrafica S.p.A., Verona

INDEX

"WHEN YOU HAVE A SPARE MOMENT, I'D LIKE
TO RAISE THE SUBJECT OF INVASION OF
PERSONAL SPACE" SPLUTTERED OLAF

ROGER RECOGNIZED GOOD DESIGN
THE MOMENT HE SAW IT

"JUST WHAT IS YOUR CANDID OPINION OF
MY FIRST VOLUME OF LOVE POETRY, OLAF?"

UNFORTUNATELY, LUNCH WAS SERVED
ALMOST IMMEDIATELY

DENTAL HYGIENE HAD NEVER BEEN
ONE OF SVEN'S STRONG POINTS

SPENDING THE NIGHT WITH SCOTT
HAD CLEARLY NOT BEEN SUCH
A GOOD IDEA AFTER ALL

10

TOGETHER WE MADE SHORT WORK OF
SUPERINTENDENT SNEDWERT'S TOUPEE

"EVER SEEN A WIMPLE UP REAL CLOSE,
YOUNG FELLOW?" WHISPERED THE BOSUN

FEARFUL OF A DESCENT INTO MORAL DECAY
WE KEPT A CLOSE WATCH ON EACH OTHER
THROUGHOUT THOSE LONG TROPICAL NIGHTS

"I'VE LISTENED TO YOUR ALIBI, M^cGURKE
AND, QUITE FRANKLY, I DON'T LIKE IT ONE
LITTLE BIT!" DRAWLED DETECTIVE HOBBS

JIM'S REQUEST FOR A TOUCH MORE SUGAR
IS MET WITH DAPHNE'S SULLEN DISAPPROVAL

THINGS JUST DIDN'T SEEM TO BE
GOING ROB'S WAY...

CLIVE'S REQUEST FOR A LIGHTLY COOKED
OMELETTE IS DEALT WITH BY THE HEAD
CHEF WITH ALL HIS CUSTOMARY FINESSE

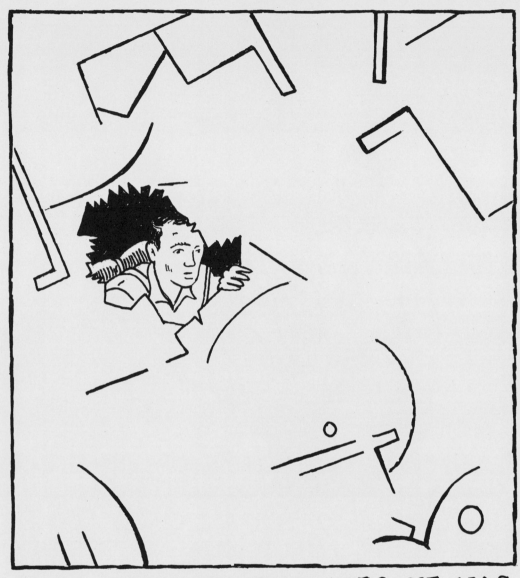

JACK SUDDENLY REALIZES HE HAS
INADVERTENTLY BLUNDERED INTO
A WORK OF TOTAL ABSTRACTION

18

I MANAGED TO SUPPLEMENT MY
MEAGRE EARNINGS WITH A LUCRATIVE
SIDELINE IN TOFU SMUGGLING

THE POLICE HAD BEEN CALLED IN TO INVESTIGATE AN OUTBREAK
OF SURREALISM IN THE VICINITY OF LOWER LETCHWORTH

ALL 1 HAD TO DO NOW WAS
TO COAX THEM INTO THE NET

"WITH THIS MINIMAL INVESTMENT I CAN MAKE THE CAREER SWITCH TO ACCOUNTANCY" EXPLAINED DOREEN

TEX HUNKERED DOWN RIGHT
UP CLOSE TO THE HEPWORTH

JUST 48 HOURS AFTER MAKING A
RESERVATION ON THE INTERNET, TIM
ARRIVES FOR HIS WEEKEND BREAK

"THAT AIN'T NO DANG-BLASTED ROTHKO!"
CORRECTED BIG JED

ON THE EIGHTH DAY AN OUTBREAK
OF LITOTES ALMOST PLUNGED OUR
VERY SURVIVAL INTO JEOPARDY

ALREADY I WAS BEGINNING TO HARBOUR
SERIOUS MISGIVINGS ABOUT DAN'S NEW
EXPRESS HAIR GROOMING SERVICE

THE BIDDLECOMBE DEFENCE HAD CLEARLY
NOT YET COME TO TERMS WITH THE
VAGARIES OF OUR PITCH

I WAS SOON TO LEARN THE FULL
DEPTH OF HIS APPALLING DEPRAVITY

TEX INCHED HIS WAY NERVOUSLY
TOWARDS THE OFFENDING BAGEL

ASKING BRENDA TO PREPARE THE SPROUTS
HAD CLEARLY BEEN MY FIRST BIG MISTAKE

I SENSED OUR RELATIONSHIP MIGHT
BE ENTERING A NEW AND POSSIBLY
TROUBLESOME PERIOD

THE EXTENSIVE REWRITES CONTINUED
RIGHT UP TO THE FINAL CURTAIN

I SPENT MANY HAPPY YEARS HELPING MY
FATHER TO SUPPLY EVERY RESTAURANT
IN OSLO WITH QUALITY TOOTHPICKS

"IT'S CALLED POLENTA, MY LIEGE
AND I'M AFRAID IT HAS ALREADY
CREPT ONTO TONIGHT'S MENU"

AS A SPECIAL TREAT, WE WERE
ALLOWED TO ACCOMPANY THE HEAD
BOY ON HIS HALF-TERM SKIING TRIP

THE FACT THAT THEY MIGHT ALSO SING
REMAINED A GRIM POSSIBILITY

37

I WAS ABLE TO DEDUCE QUITE QUICKLY
THAT I APPEARED TO HAVE LANDED
ON A FAIRLY SMALL PLANET

RUMOURS HAD BEEN CIRCULATING THAT
A LIGHT CONTINENTAL BREAKFAST
WAS ABOUT TO BE SERVED...

"HOLD ON TIGHT, FORBES. IT'S OUR ONLY CHANCE OF ESCAPE!" ROARED McEWEN

I COULD SEE AT A GLANCE HE HAD
NOTHING TO SAY

"AS A JUNIOR PARTNER YOU'LL BE EXPECTED TO WORK IN HERE" EXPLAINED HOPKINS

THERE SEEMED TO BE SOMETHING SLIGHTLY
DISCONCERTING ABOUT THE NEW NEIGHBOURS

PAM & EDDY LESKETH
The Yodelling Omelette Makers
Chichester Astoria March 16 – April 4ᵗʰ 1996

"WITH THE ECONOMY IN SUCH POOR SHAPE
MANY OF US PIRATES OPT FOR JOB-SHARING"
EXPLAINED THE POSTMAN

JUST A FEW MINUTES OUT ON OUR MAIDEN
VOYAGE, I SPOTTED A MAJOR DESIGN FAULT

RUTH WAS NOT ONE TO CONDONE
AFTER-DINNER SMOKING

IT DIDN'T TAKE ME TOO LONG TO WORK OUT ST. DRUNWERTS' GAME PLAN

"LET ME EXPLAIN HOW THIS WORKS"
ANNOUNCED PROFESSOR DRUNDLE

ROBIN WAS PROVING TO BE VERY
USEFUL AROUND THE HOUSE

KEVIN HAD A PLAN. SIMPLE
YET UNDENIABLY EFFECTIVE

"THE WAY I FIGURE IT, EITHER WAY WE'RE DOOMED" SPLUTTERED KEN

"MIGHT I BE CORRECT IN ASSUMING THIS IS YOUR FIRST GROUSE SHOOT, FORBES?" SNAPPED THREEVES

MARK CERTAINLY WAS A STICKLER
FOR PERSONAL HYGIENE

HE SPOKE UNFLINCHINGLY OF HIS TWELVE — MINUTE ORDEAL WITH THE TULIP

UNCLE BOB SEEMED KEEN TO INTRODUCE
ME TO THE JOYS OF SEA FISHING

MY SCIENTIFIC EDUCATION HAD
BEEN PLACED IN THE CAPABLE HANDS
OF GREAT UNCLE GILBERT

THE NEW SCHOOL CURRICULUM MEANT
WE NOW HAD A DOUBLE PERIOD OF
SABOTAGE EVERY THURSDAY

TUESDAY EVENING WAS NOT THE BEST
TIME TO DROP IN ON THE BRADSHAWS

I LIKE TO THINK THAT I PLAYED A SMALL
BUT SIGNIFICANT PART IN HIS VICTORY

ASKING TOM TO FRESHEN UP THE SALAD BOWL
WAS CLEARLY NOT SUCH A GOOD IDEA AFTER ALL

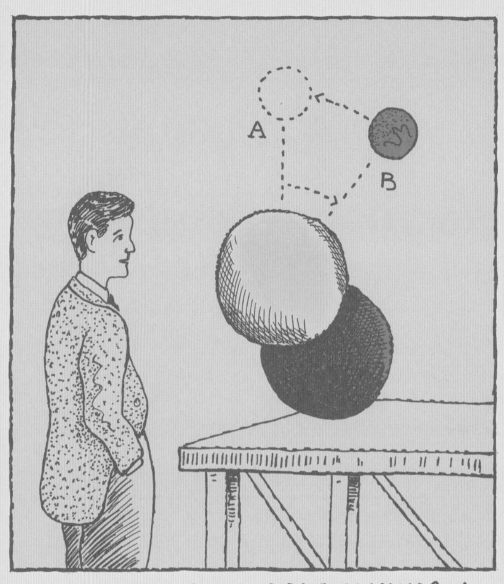

BRIAN, AS USUAL, WAS HAVING A
LITTLE DIFFICULTY WITH THE MENU

IT WAS AT SUMMER CAMP I FIRST
BEGAN TO REALIZE THE POTENTIAL
OF A CAREER IN ACCOUNTANCY

"THERE'S NO NEED TO WORRY, JENKINS. I CAN ASSURE YOU THIS EQUIPMENT HAS BEEN THOROUGHLY TESTED."

THE BOYS WASTED NO TIME IN SETTLING
IN TO THEIR NEW APARTMENT

66

Topping the bill at the Runcorn Hippodrome
October 14th 1956 — LESTER BIGHELHOF II
AND HIS AMPLIFIED PLANK

I REMEMBER WELL THE ARRIVAL OF THE
FIRST PORTABLE TELEVISION IN BRISBANE

"I CAN'T BEGIN TO TELL YOU JUST HOW MUCH I ENJOY THESE LONG WEEKEND BREAKS, LADS" BARKED UNCLE BOB

HE SEEMED TO THINK I HAD
NEVER SWEPT A FLOOR BEFORE

WITH JUST ONE APPLICATION OF QUICK-DRYING
CEMENT, LUCY WAS ABLE TO BRING THE
SERENADE TO A BLISSFUL CONCLUSION

"I SUPPOSE YOU REALIZE THIS SHADOW IS ILLEGAL?" BARKED THE BOSUN

RUMOURS WERE ALREADY CIRCULATING THAT
THE MATCH MIGHT HAVE BEEN FIXED

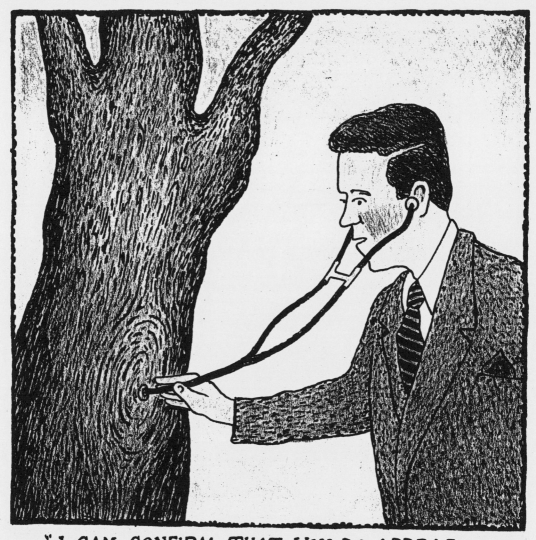

"I CAN CONFIRM THAT YOU DO APPEAR
TO HAVE A SLIGHT PROBLEM, MR. BROWN"

WAY OUT IN CHEYENNE TERRITORY, THE FIRST TEST IS NOT GOING AT ALL WELL

"ARE YOU READY TO EMBRACE VEGETARIANISM?"
SNAPPED THE REGULATOR

WITHHOLDING BARRY'S GOURD SEEMED
TO PROVIDE TREVOR WITH AN
UNPARALLELED DEGREE OF SATISFACTION

"I DON'T THINK THIS TECHNICALLY QUALIFIES AS A STETSON, DEAR" BARKED BRENDA

AS A MUSIC LOVER I FELT IT MY DUTY
TO DIRECT THE DISINTEGRATOR RAY
OVER THE ENTIRE GLEE CLUB

"FROM HERE ON IN I MUST FACE THIS GRUELLING
ORDEAL ALONE, BUT I PROMISE WHEN I
EVENTUALLY EMERGE I'LL BE RETURNING
TO YOU LADS A MORE COMPLETE HUMAN
BEING" PLEDGED MR EVANSTON

THINGS HAD BEEN GOING QUITE WELL
FOR ME RIGHT UP UNTIL THE SECOND
MINUTE OF ROUND SEVEN...

"JUST HOW MANY PAIRS OF EARRINGS WILL YOU ACTUALLY NEED ON THIS VOYAGE?" SNAPPED THE FIRST MATE

FOLLOWING THE INCIDENT OF THE
TRAMPLED SNOOD, COMMUNICATIONS AT
Nº 48 REMAINED SOMEWHAT STRAINED

"I'M A FIRM BELIEVER IN TRADITION. TUESDAY MEANS LINGUINE" EXPLAINED THE TYRANT

MR. UNSWORTH'S INABILITY TO SHARE HIS
TRIANGLES BEGAN TO CREATE AN
ATMOSPHERE OF SEETHING RESENTMENT
AMONGST HIS FELLOW BASSOONISTS

"THOSE DANGED CLOUDS JUST DON'T
LOOK RIGHT!" MUSED CRAIG

"AS YOUR BIRTHDAY TREAT, YOUR MOTHER AND
I HAVE DECIDED TO PACK YOU OFF TO BORNEO
FOR A COUPLE OF YEARS" EXPLAINED MY FATHER

I WAS MERELY DOING MY BEST TO
BUILD UP DEREK'S CONFIDENCE

NOT EVEN THE INTIMIDATING FIGURE
OF MISS HOLLINGSWORTH, HEAD OF
NEEDLEWORK, COULD STOP HER NOW

"I'LL BE TAKING YOUR ORDER SOMETIME IN THE FORSEEABLE FUTURE" SNAPPED THE MARTINET

I SENSED OUR LITTLE DEBATE MIGHT
BE DRAWING TO A CLOSE

DAN RETURNS HOME TO FIND
LITTLE HAS CHANGED

I BEGAN TO REALIZE THAT OUR
DEFENCE MIGHT WELL BE IN TROUBLE

I SOON BEGAN TO REALIZE I HAD BEEN ASSIGNED
TO A CRACK UNIT OF MILITARY INTELLIGENCE

BIG AL WASN'T ABOUT TO TAKE ANY CHANCES

ROBINSON BARELY SKIMMED THE DELACROIX
AS HE MADE HIS WAY HOME THAT NIGHT

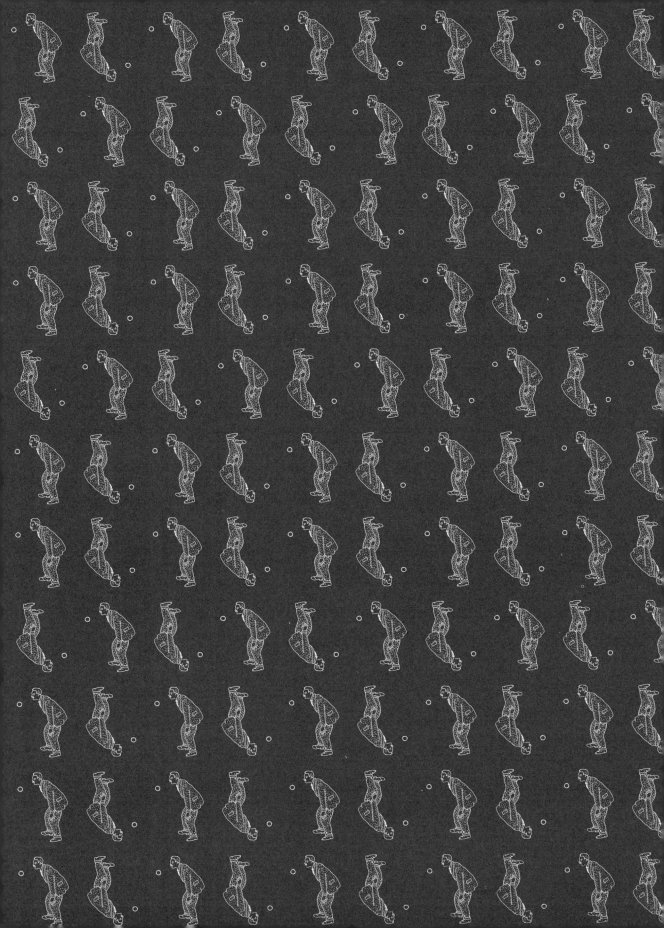